Clarinet
Exam Pieces

ABRSM Grade 5

Selected from the 2014–2017 syllabus

Name S. Bl

Date of exam

CW00347553

Contents

Footnotes: Anthony Burton and Colin Lawson (CL)

Other pieces for Grade 5

First published in 2013 by ABRSM (Publishing) Ltd, a wholly owned subsidiary of ABRSM, 24 Portland Place, London W1B 1LU, United Kingdom © 2013 by The Associated Board of the Royal Schools of Music

Music origination by Julia Bovee
Cover by Kate Benjamin & Andy Potts
Printed in England by Halstan & Co. Ltd, Amersham, Bucks.

MIX
Paper from responsible sources
FSC™ C109619

A:1

Andante quasi allegretto

Edited by Colin Lawson

Léo Delibes
(1836–91)

From the 1870s until the First World War, end-of-year competitions, or examinations, at the Paris Conservatoire included a sight-reading test with piano accompaniment, for which the music was specially written by one of the conservatoire's professors of composition. The test piece for clarinet in July 1877 was written by Léo Delibes, the composer of the ballets *Coppélia* and *Sylvia* and the opera *Lakmé* (which includes the well-known 'Flower Duet'). His piece requires precision in its recurring rhythmic figure, though its aim is not simply to examine correctness but also to encourage an expressive and musical performance. CL

Source: autograph manuscript, Paris, Archives nationales, AJ[37] 198, 2

A:2

Allegro moderato

First movement from Sonata No. 6 in B flat

Edited by and continuo
realization by Colin Lawson

Xavier Lefèvre
(1763–1829)

The Swiss-born clarinettist Xavier Lefèvre was appointed to the staff of the Paris Conservatoire when it was founded in 1795 in the wake of the French Revolution. At first the clarinet department was the largest in the conservatoire, with 19 professors appointed to teach 104 pupils. Tutors were soon published for each instrument and Lefèvre's *Méthode de Clarinette* dates from 1802. In his text he reminds students that they must make the clarinet sing and he emphasizes how important it is to communicate with an audience. At the end of the method are 12 three-movement sonatas that are both attractive and challenging. They were originally written for clarinet with just a bass line (probably cello), but are now often played with keyboard, as in the version presented here. In his tutor, Lefèvre makes a distinction between the staccato dot (·) and the wedge (ʼ). The dot represents a lightly tongued short note; the wedge should be given more emphasis and indicates a note of equal weight to those which surround it.

The source has a staccato dot on the penultimate clarinet note of bar 28, but since this seems to be an error it has been omitted here. In the edition printed here, broken slur lines indicate editorial extensions of existing slurs. CL

Source: *Méthode de Clarinette* (Paris, 1802), facsimile edition, Minkoff, 1974

A:3

Der Schottenclan

No. 3 from *Schottische Bilder*, Op. 112

Edited by Colin Lawson

Carl Loewe
(1796–1869)

Allegretto, alla marcia [♩ = c.108]

Der Schottenclan The Scottish Clan; **Schottische Bilder** Scottish Pictures

The German composer Carl Loewe is now chiefly remembered for his vast output of songs, although he also wrote operas, oratorios and piano pieces, as well as a small amount of chamber music. Loewe's set of three miniatures entitled *Scottish Pictures* was dedicated to his son-in-law Arthur of Bothwell, an amateur clarinettist. Published in 1850, these pieces were (unusually for the time) originally scored for C clarinet. They offer some modest insights into the Romantic view of Scotland represented on a much grander scale in Mendelssohn's Scottish Symphony and his *Hebrides* overture. Loewe's representation of 'The Scottish Clan' needs to be played with special verve and energy. CL
Source: *Schottische Bilder*, Op. 112 (Berlin: Schlesinger, 1850)

Andantino

Second movement from Sonatina, Op. 29

Malcolm Arnold
(1921–2006)

The British composer Malcolm Arnold is best known for his film scores and for his orchestral light music, such as the two sets of *English Dances*, though he also composed nine symphonies. Early in his career, he wrote a series of sonatinas (little sonatas) for woodwind instruments and piano. The Sonatina for clarinet was written in 1951 with the playing of the well-known clarinettist Frederick Thurston in mind; but it was first performed by Thurston's pupil Colin Davis, shortly before he began his career as a conductor. The work consists of two brilliant quick movements separated by this gentler Andantino, which is frequently performed at a slower tempo than Arnold's suggested metronome mark. With its main theme – melody and accompaniment – using only the notes of (sounding) C major, this movement is a good example of Arnold's ability to make something fresh and individual out of traditional ways of writing.

© 1951 by Alfred Lengnick & Co. Ltd

Reproduced by permission of Universal Music Publishing MGB Ltd. All enquiries about this piece, apart from those directly relating to the exams, should be addressed to Universal Music Publishing MGB Ltd, 20 Fulham Broadway, London SW6 1AH.

B:2

Circle Dance

No. 6 from *Suite hébraïque No. 1*

S. I. Glick
(1934–2002)

Suite hébraïque Hebrew Suite

Srul Irving Glick was a Canadian composer, who worked for many years as a music producer for the Canadian Broadcasting Corporation. The son of a Russian-born synagogue cantor (Jewish liturgical singer), he was heavily influenced by Jewish musical traditions. His compositions include six *Suites hébraïques* for various combinations of instruments. The first was written in 1961 as an orchestral work, and arranged two years later for clarinet or soprano saxophone and piano. Its finale is a 'Circle Dance' in changing metres. The quaver pulse should remain constant.

Clarinet Exam Pieces

ABRSM Grade 5

Selected from the 2014–2017 syllabus

Piano accompaniment

Contents

Footnotes: Anthony Burton and Colin Lawson (CL)

The pieces in this album have been taken from a variety of different sources. Where appropriate, they have been checked with original source material and edited to help the player when preparing for performance. Any editorial additions are given in small print; within square brackets; or, in the case of slurs and ties, in the form ⌢. Details of other editorial amendments or suggestions are given in the footnotes. Breath marks (retained here where they appear in the source edition) and all editorial additions are for guidance only; they are not comprehensive or obligatory. Descriptive titles are given in their original language, and translations into English appear above the footnotes.

ABRSM Clarinet Exams: requirements

Pieces
In the exam, candidates must play three pieces, one chosen from each of the three syllabus lists (A, B and C). Candidates are free to choose from the pieces printed in this album and/or from the other pieces set for the grade: a full list is given in the clarinet part with this score as well as in the 2014–2017 Woodwind syllabus.

Scales and arpeggios
Sight-reading
Aural tests
} Full details are available online at www.abrsm.org/clarinet5 or in the 2014–2017 Woodwind syllabus booklet.

First published in 2013 by ABRSM (Publishing) Ltd, a wholly owned subsidiary of ABRSM, 24 Portland Place, London W1B 1LU, United Kingdom

© 2013 by The Associated Board of the Royal Schools of Music

Music origination by Julia Bovee
Cover by Kate Benjamin & Andy Potts
Printed in England by Halstan & Co. Ltd, Amersham, Bucks.

Andante quasi allegretto

Edited by Colin Lawson

Léo Delibes
(1836–91)

From the 1870s until the First World War, end-of-year competitions, or examinations, at the Paris Conservatoire included a sight-reading test with piano accompaniment, for which the music was specially written by one of the conservatoire's professors of composition. The test piece for clarinet in July 1877 was written by Léo Delibes, the composer of the ballets *Coppélia* and *Sylvia* and the opera *Lakmé* (which includes the well-known 'Flower Duet'). His piece requires precision in its recurring rhythmic figure, though its aim is not simply to examine correctness but also to encourage an expressive and musical performance. CL

Source: autograph manuscript, Paris, Archives nationales, AJ[37] 198, 2

A:2

Allegro moderato

First movement from Sonata No. 6 in B flat

Edited by and continuo
realization by Colin Lawson

Xavier Lefèvre
(1763–1829)

The Swiss-born clarinettist Xavier Lefèvre was appointed to the staff of the Paris Conservatoire when it was founded in 1795 in the wake of the French Revolution. At first the clarinet department was the largest in the conservatoire, with 19 professors appointed to teach 104 pupils. Tutors were soon published for each instrument and Lefèvre's *Méthode de Clarinette* dates from 1802. In his text he reminds students that they must make the clarinet sing and he emphasizes how important it is to communicate with an audience. At the end of the method are 12 three-movement sonatas that are both attractive and challenging. They were originally written for clarinet with just a bass line (probably cello), but are now often played with keyboard, as in the version presented here. In his tutor, Lefèvre makes a distinction between the staccato dot (·) and the wedge (ꞌ). The dot represents a lightly tongued short note; the wedge should be given more emphasis and indicates a note of equal weight to those which surround it.

The slurs in the bass part in bars 5, 6 and 53 end on the crotchet in the source, but have been shortened here by analogy with those in bars 9 and 10. The source also has a staccato dot on the penultimate clarinet note of bar 28 and a staccato wedge on the third note of bar 45 in the bass part, but since these seem to be errors they have been omitted here. In the edition printed here, broken slur lines indicate editorial extensions of existing slurs. CL

Source: *Méthode de Clarinette* (Paris, 1802), facsimile edition, Minkoff, 1974

Der Schottenclan

No. 3 from *Schottische Bilder*, Op. 112

Edited by Colin Lawson

Carl Loewe
(1796–1869)

Der Schottenclan The Scottish Clan; **Schottische Bilder** Scottish Pictures

The German composer Carl Loewe is now chiefly remembered for his vast output of songs, although he also wrote operas, oratorios and piano pieces, as well as a small amount of chamber music. Loewe's set of three miniatures entitled *Scottish Pictures* was dedicated to his son-in-law Arthur of Bothwell, an amateur clarinettist. Published in 1850, these pieces were (unusually for the time) originally scored for C clarinet. They offer some modest insights into the Romantic view of Scotland represented on a much grander scale in Mendelssohn's Scottish Symphony and his *Hebrides* overture. Loewe's representation of 'The Scottish Clan' needs to be played with special verve and energy.

In bar 114, piano left hand, the final two chords in the source are E flat minor root position triads (as at the beginning of the bar) but they have been changed here to B flat major first inversion triads (to match the final three chords of bar 113) by analogy with bars 54, 58, 66, 110 and 122. CL
Source: *Schottische Bilder*, Op. 112 (Berlin: Schlesinger, 1850)

Andantino

Second movement from Sonatina, Op. 29

Malcolm Arnold
(1921–2006)

The British composer Malcolm Arnold is best known for his film scores and for his orchestral light music, such as the two sets of *English Dances*, though he also composed nine symphonies. Early in his career, he wrote a series of sonatinas (little sonatas) for woodwind instruments and piano. The Sonatina for clarinet was written in 1951 with the playing of the well-known clarinettist Frederick Thurston in mind; but it was first performed by Thurston's pupil Colin Davis, shortly before he began his career as a conductor. The work consists of two brilliant quick movements separated by this gentler Andantino, which is frequently performed at a slower tempo than Arnold's suggested metronome mark. With its main theme – melody and accompaniment – using only the notes of (sounding) C major, this movement is a good example of Arnold's ability to make something fresh and individual out of traditional ways of writing.

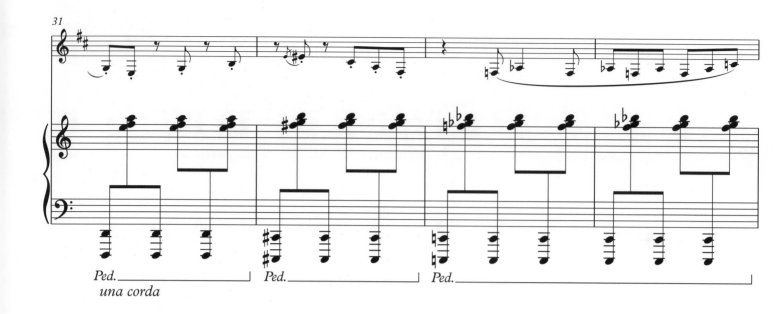

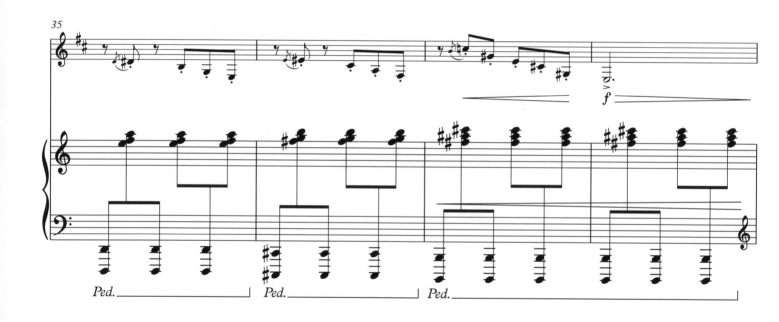

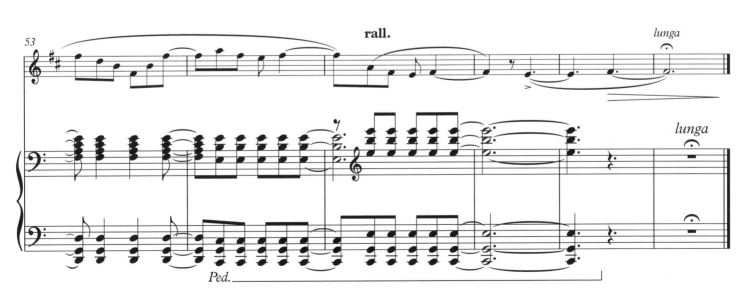

B:2

Circle Dance

No. 6 from *Suite hébraïque No. 1*

S. I. Glick
(1934–2002)

Suite hébraïque Hebrew Suite

Srul Irving Glick was a Canadian composer, who worked for many years as a music producer for the Canadian Broadcasting Corporation. The son of a Russian-born synagogue cantor (Jewish liturgical singer), he was heavily influenced by Jewish musical traditions. His compositions include six *Suites hébraïques* for various combinations of instruments. The first was written in 1961 as an orchestral work, and arranged two years later for clarinet or soprano saxophone and piano. Its finale is a 'Circle Dance' in changing metres. The quaver pulse should remain constant.

Reproduced by permission of Boosey & Hawkes Music Publishers Ltd. All enquiries about this piece, apart from those directly relating to the exams, should be addressed to Boosey & Hawkes Music Publishers Ltd, Aldwych House, 71–91 Aldwych, London WC2B 4HN.

AB 3689

Duo I

from *El sueño de una noche de verano*

B:3

Arranged by Hywel Davies

Astor Piazzolla
(1921–92)

El sueño de una noche de verano A Midsummer Night's Dream

Astor Piazzolla was a major figure in the development of the tango (the Argentinian national dance) as a player of the bandoneón (or button accordion), a leader of groups of various sizes, and a composer. In the later part of his career, he collaborated with classical orchestras and classical and jazz soloists all over the world. In 1986, he wrote music for a modern-dress production of Shakespeare's *A Midsummer Night's Dream* by the Comédie-Française, the French national theatre company, in Paris. The tempo direction of this duo suggests that it should be played throughout with some rhythmic freedom, as if it were being improvised.

   The passage marked *quasi cadenza* in bar 17 should be played in the exam.

Duo I

from *El sueño de una noche de verano*

Arranged by Hywel Davies

Astor Piazzolla
(1921–92)

El sueño de una noche de verano A Midsummer Night's Dream

Astor Piazzolla was a major figure in the development of the tango (the Argentinian national dance) as a player of the bandoneón (or button accordion), a leader of groups of various sizes, and a composer. In the later part of his career, he collaborated with classical orchestras and classical and jazz soloists all over the world. In 1986, he wrote music for a modern-dress production of Shakespeare's *A Midsummer Night's Dream* by the Comédie-Française, the French national theatre company, in Paris. The tempo direction of this duo suggests that it should be played throughout with some rhythmic freedom, as if it were being improvised.

The passage marked *quasi cadenza* in bar 17 should be played in the exam.

poco rubato · a tempo · rit.

quasi cadenza · accel. · molto rit. · [a tempo] · poco *f*

poco *f*

poco *f* · più *f*

poco *f* · poco *f*

poco rubato · a tempo · molto rit. · *pp*

C:1

The Heron Glides

No. 4 from *Somerset Scenes for Solo Clarinet*

Colin Cowles
(born 1940)

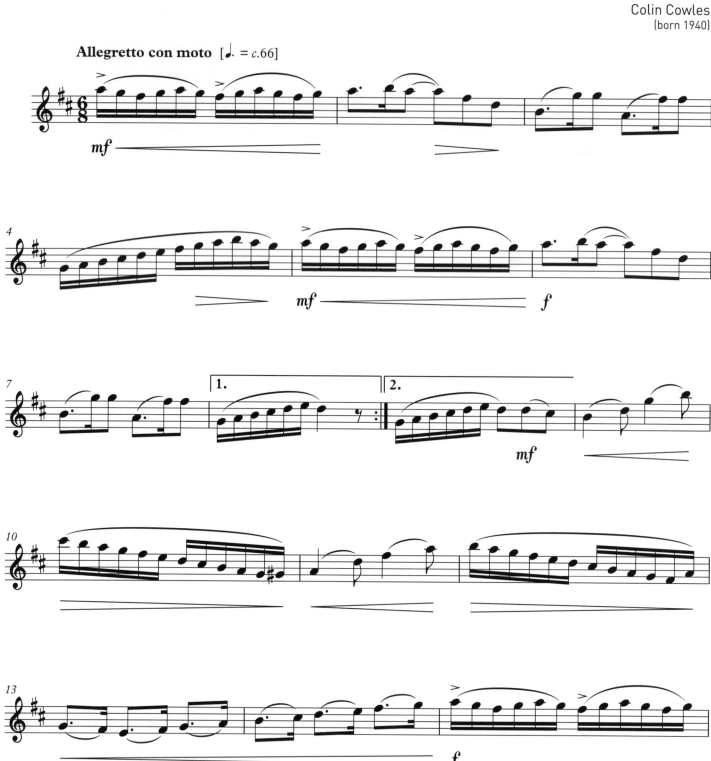

Colin Cowles spent the early part of his life in the home counties around London, as a schoolteacher and then as a teacher of woodwind instruments, and also as an examiner and composer. Since 1991 he has lived on the Somerset Levels, a wetland area of south-west England. Among his more than 400 compositions is *Somerset Scenes*, a suite of 'five impressions for unaccompanied clarinet' published in 1997. 'The Heron Glides' is a study suggested by the flight of that large and beautiful bird.

Exercise in C

C:2

No. 32 from '45 Exercices sur différentes combinaisons d'articulation'
from *Méthode pour servir à l'enseignement de la Clarinette*

H. E. Klosé
(1808–80)

Méthode pour servir à l'enseignement de la Clarinette Method for Teaching the Clarinet

Hyacinthe Eléonore Klosé was born on the Greek island of Corfu, but moved to Paris to play the clarinet in a regimental band, and in 1831 began studying at the Paris Conservatoire. He later taught at the conservatoire for nearly 30 years, while also playing in the opera orchestra of the Italian Theatre. He made an important contribution to the development of the modern 'Boehm system' clarinet. Klosé published solo pieces for clarinet, studies for clarinet and saxophone, and a teaching method for clarinet that is still in use today. It includes a series of '45 Exercises in different combinations of articulation' – among them this piece, No. 32 in C major. Dynamics are left to the player's discretion.

Source: *Méthode pour servir à l'enseignement de la Clarinette à anneaux mobiles, et de celle à 13 clés* (Paris: E. Gérard et Cie, éditeurs Ancienne Maison Meissonnier, *c.*1845)

C:3

Samba Diablo

No. 19 from *21st-Century Clarinet Studies*

Colin Radford
(born 1959)

Colin Radford was a member of the Grenadier Guards Band for 22 years then studied at Anglia Ruskin University in Cambridge; he is now a freelance composer. His compositions include a set of *21st-Century Clarinet Studies*, which he describes as 'using musical devices from various cultures, such as pentatonic, modal and diminished scales, elements of traditional and be-bop jazz, Celtic folk and Latin-American dance forms'. The title of this study combines the name of a syncopated Brazilian dance and the Spanish word for 'devil'. About the piece, Colin Radford says: 'The crescendo from the first bar should be easy since the melody jumps an octave with each successive bar, from the softer chalumeau up to the brighter middle register. The figure at bar 25 moves around the break a fair bit and is probably the most difficult part to keep steady. You should be able to give the last three bars some impact.'